The Travelling Leunig

Michael Leunig's words and picture were first
published in Australia in 1965. He was born
in Melbourne and now lives on a farm in
north-eastern Victoria.

The Travelling Leunig comprises pieces that
have previously appeared in the Melbourne *Age*
and the *Sydney Morning Herald*.

Also by Michael Leunig

The Travelling Leunig

cartoons by Michael Leunig

PENGUIN BOOKS

PENGUIN BOOKS

Published by the Penguin Group
Penguin Group (Australia)
250 Camberwell Road, Camberwell, Victoria 3124, Australia
(a division of Pearson Australia Group Pty Ltd)
Penguin Group (USA) Inc.
375 Hudson Street, New York, New York 10014, USA
Penguin Group (Canada)
90 Eglinton Avenue East, Suite 700, Toronto, ON M4P 2Y3, Canada
(a division of Pearson Penguin Canada Inc.)
Penguin Books Ltd
80 Strand, London WC2R 0RL, England
Penguin Ireland
25 St Stephen's Green, Dublin 2, Ireland
(a division of Penguin Books Ltd)
Penguin Books India Pvt Ltd
11, Community Centre, Panchsheel Park, New Delhi-110 017, India
Penguin Group (NZ)
Cnr Airborne and Rosedale Roads, Albany, Auckland, New Zealand
(a division of Pearson New Zealand Ltd)
Penguin Books (South Africa) (Pty) Ltd
24 Sturdee Avenue, Rosebank, Johannesburg 2196, South Africa

Penguin Books Ltd, Registered Offices: 80 Strand, London WC2R 0RL, England

First published by Penguin Books Australia Ltd 1990
19 18 17 16 15 14 13 12
Copyright © Michael Leunig, 1990

Printed and bound in China by Bookbuilders

National Library of Australia
Cataloguing-in-Publication data:

Leunig, Michael, 1945– .
The Travelling Leunig.

ISBN-13: 978 014 014867 1
ISBN-10: 0 14 014867 1

1. Australian wit and humor, Pictorial. 2. Caricatures
and cartoons – Australia. I. Title.

741.5994

www.penguin.com.au

Let it go. Let it out.
Let it all unravel.
Let it free and it can be
A path on which to travel.

Leunig

Driving his trusty Curlymobile and accompanied by his direction-finding duck,
Mr Curly takes the dangerous, winding road back to his childhood on an
important mission. In the darkness he negotiates the flimsy bridge over the
Great Gap. In front of him, in the glow of the headlights, Mr Curly sees wondrous
shapes emerging from the gloom. Somewhere in the blackness a bell tolls.
He has arrived!

HOW TO GET THERE

Go to the end of the path until you get to the gate.

Go through the gate and head straight out towards the horizon.

Keep going towards the horizon.

Sit down and have
a rest every now
and again.

But keep on going.
Just keep on with it.

Keep on going as
far as you can.
That's how you
get there

Leunig

THE OLD WAYS ..... THE TRUE WAYS.

A GOOD RESTAURANT TABLE ALWAYS HAS one leg shorter than the others so THAT it requires a folded napkin under it to achieve the stability necessary for secure and comfortable dining. THIS SHORTENING IS CREATED by a craftsperson using only a SPOKESHAVE, a true eye and the skill Handed down through generations of TABLE LEG SHORTENERS.

Leunig

THE INVENTION OF THE PEDESTAL.

Leunig

CHRISTMAS TELEPHONES

cordless car phone

teapot phone

phone with memory, redial and pop-up toaster

redial phone with zoom lens, auto focus and cordless electric screwdriver

phone with calculator, auto-teller, video game five time zones coffee brewer with graphic equalizer

Bicentennial laser phone with aloe vera, water resist to 50M. with bar coding quartz-halogen compact disc nervous breakdown with four-wheel-drive solar heated swimming pool.

leunig

The election trail. The hustings. The democratic process.

"*This? This is a firestick! I made it on my desk at the office by rubbing two pencils together.
The secretaries kept it going all day in a wastepaper bin. Deborah . . . here is my home, you are
my wife and this is my firestick. I'm so happy I could die.*"

I'M STOCKPILING
WEAPONS TO DEFEND
THE CAVE....

YOU'LL HAVE TO
MAKE ROOM...

NOW I'M MAKING A STOCKPILE
TO DEFEND THE STOCKPILE...
YOU'LL HAVE TO MAKE MORE ROOM.

IT'S A DETERRENT...

IT CERTAINLY
IS.....

Leunig

Between the whimper and the bang
Life is like a boomerang.

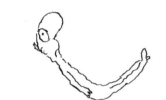

Thrown by some great hairy hand.
Spinning out across the land.

Spinning out across the years
Spinning lies and spinning tears

Spinning heart and spinning brain
Spinning pleasure, spinning pain

Spinning out and spinning round
And spinning back towards the ground.

A graceful loop across the land
Then back into the hairy hand.

Leunig

THE LIFE CYCLE OF THE SUPERMARKET TROLLEY

SUPERMARKET TROLLEYS COME ASHORE UNDER THE FULL MOON TO LAY THEIR EGGS IN THE SAND

WHEN THE EGGS HATCH THE YOUNG TROLLEYS MAKE THEIR WAY TO THE SUPERMARKET WHERE THEY ASSEMBLE IN THE CARPARK.

NOW THEY BEGIN THEIR STRANGE LIFE ENGULFING AND DISGORGING VAST QUANTITIES OF CONSUMER ITEMS

AFTER SEVERAL YEARS, WHEN THEY HAVE REACHED MATURITY, THE TROLLEYS ESCAPE INDIVIDUALLY INTO THE SURROUNDING STREETS

AND BY VARIOUS ROUTES, DRAINS, CANALS, RIVERS, THEY MAKE THEIR WAY BACK TO THE SEA

WHERE THEY MATE IN DEEP WATER AND WAIT FOR FULL MOON TO BEGIN THE CYCLE ALL OVER AGAIN. ETC.

Leunig

HAIR
RESTORER

DO NOT
SNIFF

"We're Church of England aren't we?"

There was once an inventor whose work it was to invent new dances.

His aim was to invent the perfect dance which is, of course, an impossibility.

At the end of each day, enraged with frustration he would fling his day's work out to the street in disgust.

The peasants of the town would seize upon these imperfect dances and dance them with great joy and gusto.

The inventor worked on in earnest dedication. Alone.

The peasants danced their lives away. Together. Life goes on.

<u>1988</u>   Dear diary.... it could be the greenhouse effect but what a strange early Spring! The old plum tree is already in blossom and what blossoms! Instead of pale pink flowers there is a weird assortment of objects where those delicate petals used to be. There's a vast selection of sushi.... small pieces of raw fish all over the tree. And morsels of rice wrapped in seaweed.... and chopsticks too. There are pieces of dark polished marble and chrome and stainless steel bursting out of the wood. There are posters too... mainly Paris streetscapes with handsome men kissing beautiful women.... there are Monet prints and imitation Monet prints. There is also a lot of tricky steel furniture, mainly bar stools which look very uncomfortable and there are Porsche and B.M.W. badges galore. What has happened to our old plum tree? If these are the flowers then what fruits will we see in late summer? I dread to think.

Leunig

FOUR DEPRESSING NEW FABLES

JACK AND THE BINS TALK

HANSEL AND GRISTLE

GOLDILOCKS AND THE THREE BARS.

ALADDIN AND HIS LUMP.

Leunig

CUP EVE

Men and Women: war and peace.

You're too tense Warwick...
we'll just relax these muscles
and your shorts will SLIDE on

no worries

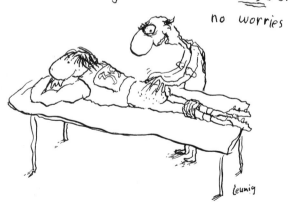

"The one on the left is a yuppy. The one on the right is a dinky. Behind them is a trendy and next to the trendy is a hippie . . . then down past the monkeys are some more dinkies looking at the donkeys."

"I can accept the fact that you've grown the antlers, Frank, I honestly can, but what I can't live with any longer is the clanking sound on the head of the bed. I can't take it any more."

♪ ♩

BARRELS BY CANDLELIGHT

On the twelfth day of Christmas my true love gave to me
TWELVE cans of beer, ELEVEN brandy crusters, TEN bloody
marys, NINE gin and tonics. EIGHT scotch and sodas,
SEVEN Brandivinos, SIX dry martinis

FIVE POTS OF RED.....
FOUR rum and cokes, THREE
tawny ports, TWO
creme de
menthes and
a wall banger
on the
front porch.

DISPRIN

Leunig

FESTIVAL OF DULL ROUTINE
FESTIVAL OF BORING LOUDMOUTHS JUNE 1-10
FESTIVAL OF DRAB COMMITTEES MAY 1 — SEP 30
FESTIVAL OF THE MUNDANE JULY 7-21
FESTIVAL OF PETTY FRUSTRATION JUNE 25 - JULY 7
FESTIVAL OF TEDIOUS OBLIGATIONS JUNE 10-24
FESTIVAL OF FATIGUE AND EXHAUSTION
JUNE 1st JULY 31st

now that you've got the COMMANDMENTS I'd like to give you the ADVICE, the SUGGESTIONS AND the HANDY HINTS ..
thanks awfully but we're only interested in the Bottom line ... these days
Leunig

leunig

HIS RADIO AERIAL HAD
BEEN SNAPPED OFF BY VANDALS
SO HE IMPROVISED. HE
REPLACED IT WITH A WIRE
COATHANGER

BEFORE DRIVING OFF
HE ABSENT-MINDEDLY
HUNG HIS COAT ON THE HANGER

UNWITTINGLY HE DROVE UNDER
A PAIR OF TROUSERS WHICH WERE
HANGING IN THE SKY

HIS CAR ROSE UP FROM THE
GROUND, THE COAT DRAWN
SKYWARD BY THE POWER OF
THE TROUSERS.

THE COAT DOCKED WITH THE
TROUSERS. HE WAS TRAPPED
IN SPACE. CAUGHT BETWEEN
HEAVEN AND HELL.

EVERY DAY LIFE WAS BECOMING
MORE DIFFICULT TO LIVE AND
HARDER TO UNDERSTAND. WAS THIS
THE LAST STRAW...? THE FINAL
HUMILIATION....?

leunig

The Curly Flat Quarale Society.

"I'm sure we'd all be perfectly happy to start using condoms. Perfectly happy! But why the heck should we have to stop sharing needles!"

THE TROUBLE WITH SHOPPING...

The shop was too elegant...

The changing room was too small... the trousers were too tight...

The mirror was too awful... the salesperson poked her head in too soon...

He tripped over too easily and rolled out into the shop too clumsily

The cleaner swept him out too unthinkingly

He landed in the industrial waste bin too rapidly...

was dumped in the rubbish tip too brutally...

where he found a pair of trousers

... which fitted absolutely PERFECTLY!

"Here's your problem, pal . . . there's an anchovy in the distributor."

THE FACTS OF LIFE. (A POEM)

WHERE DO BABIES GO TO....?

WILL SOMEBODY EXPLAIN

THEY GO INTO THE WORLD.... AND THEN...

THEY'RE NEVER SEEN AGAIN.

Leunig

Onwards and onwards. The steam-powered Curlymobile.

I have come to
sit at your feet because
I have long respected
and admired you.
I regard you as a
saint and a guru.
I want to learn
from you and
understand your
wisdom ....

As time passes I shall
begin to see through you,
your weaknesses and
fallacies and I will
grow disappointed
with you for being
merely human

Then I shall take advantage of what you have taught me and I shall be strengthened by it and use it to rise above you and be embarrassed that I ever took you seriously...

And using mockery I shall distance myself from you until eventually I shall forget that you ever existed.

Leunig

The attack of the boring graffiti artist.

FAVORITE WORN AND SHABBY DOMESTIC ITEMS

THE ARMCHAIR OF PHILOSOPHY.

THE TEAPOT OF TRUTH.

THE PILLOW OF FAITH.

THE RUG OF CONSTANCY.

THE VASE OF TRANQUILITY

THE DOG OF SANITY

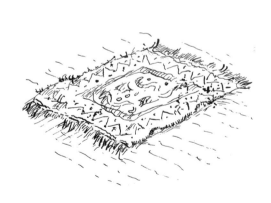

Leunig

The first condoms of Spring.

The greatest discovery of all; the invention of the weal.

HOW TO MAKE FOX SOUP

You will need :— one old fox.

Three large, woody turnips.

Snip whiskers off fox and put aside.

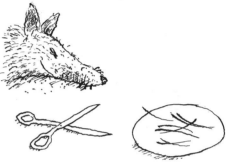

Place fox and turnips in a cauldron and simmer on a low flame for two days

Strain liquid and serve in a bowl or deep dish.

Garnish with whiskers.

N.B. THIS SOUP MAKES YOU VERY CLEVER

Leunig

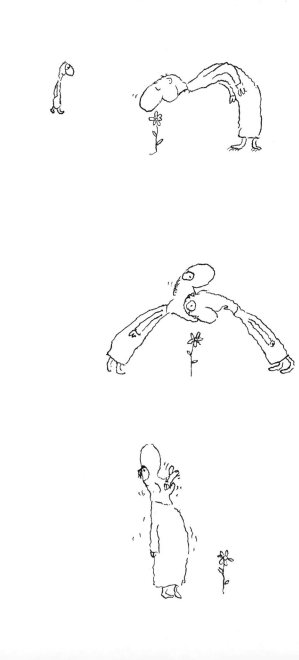

leunig

TIME TO CUT THE LONG GRASS AROUND THE HOUSE.

The call comes through about lunchtime. A big AIDS outbreak north of the town and heading this way fast.

We all jump in the cabin and fly under a blanket on the floor for protection.
All of us except Chooka.

Poor Chooka jumps in the water tank which is the worst possible thing to do. Apparently the sight of a wet body can drive these gays into a frenzy.

We all jump in the truck and fly out there and by the time we arrive things look pretty serious.

Thousands of these gay blokes are kissing and cuddling and rolling about and the whole thing's fanned by a hot, dirty north wind.

No sooner do we get the hoses on it than the wind swings round and before we know it we're surrounded.

So we just dig in while the whole dreadful thing rages over us and when it's passed we jump up and race Chooka to hospital for a checkup.

Just to be on the safe side we decide to all take the test ourselves

It turns out that Chooka gets the all clear but it seems that things could be a bit touch and go for the blokes who were under the blanket. Bit of a worry really.

Leunig

Unsatisfactory Santas .... Critical notes based on some early sightings.

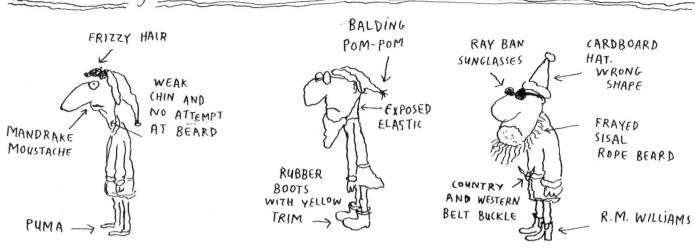

FRIZZY HAIR

WEAK CHIN AND NO ATTEMPT AT BEARD

MANDRAKE MOUSTACHE

PUMA →

BALDING POM-POM

EXPOSED ELASTIC

RUBBER BOOTS WITH YELLOW TRIM →

RAY BAN SUNGLASSES

CARDBOARD HAT. WRONG SHAPE

FRAYED SISAL ROPE BEARD

COUNTRY AND WESTERN BELT BUCKLE

R.M. WILLIAMS

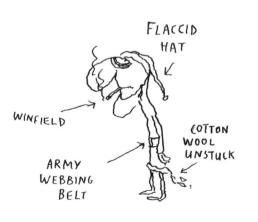

FLACCID HAT

WINFIELD →

ARMY WEBBING BELT

COTTON WOOL UNSTUCK

EAR-RING

UNBOUNTIFUL SACK

TATTOO

CONVERTED KAFTAN

···· AND THIS IS JUST THE TIP OF THE ICEBERG!

leunig

It was autumn and his heart was full and ripe and ready for plucking.

So he went to the art gallery where all the paintings were turning gold and brown. A sad and wonderful sight.

How beautiful they seemed as they fluttered from the walls. An attendant swept them into piles and set fire to them.

The pungent, evocative smell of burning art filled the crisp, morning air as he walked out onto the street.

A woman drove past with a small, pink section of her dress hem flapping from beneath the car door.

Tears of gratitude swelled from his eyes. Life indeed was sweet and rich and deep and joyous.

leunig

THE 1990 FESTIVAL OF SOBBING AND WEEPING

Nocturnal dog weeping.

Solo shoulder weeping.

Simple nude tree weeping

Primal, lavatorial sobbing.

Structured, ceremonial group weeping

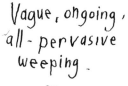

Vague, ongoing, all-pervasive weeping.

Cold, monastic candle weeping

Deep, rhythmic urban carpet sobbing.

leunig

Hold on to it like you hold a day old chicken

Hold on to it like you hold a live fish.

Hold on to it like you hold a horse.

Hold on to it like you hold a bowl of soup.

Hold on to it like you hold a door open for the Queen Mother.

Letting go of it is just as difficult and shall be dealt with at some later stage.

Leunig

When the heart
Is cut or cracked or broken
Do not clutch it
Let the wound lie open

Let the wind
From the good old sea blow in
To bathe the wound with salt
And let it sting.

Let a stray dog lick it
Let a bird lean in the hole and sing
A simple song like a tiny bell
And let it ring

Leunig

SOMETHING FOR THE SIMPLE MINDED DAYDREAMER

Nero fiddled while Rome burned !

This was seen as arrogant, indulgent and stupid.

Now if Nero had been truly smart he would have organised a fiddling CONTEST while Rome burned.

A competition!
A match! ....
A <u>FIDDLING DUEL</u>!

Nobody would have
noticed or cared if Rome
was burning. NO WAY!
Not with a match
in progress.

<u>MORAL</u>. When any sort of
contest is in progress,
turn away from it, go
to the window and look
out carefully at the world.

Leunig

Veteran's march.

GENTLEMEN....
charge your glasses for a toast...!
gentlemen...
HERE's TO THE FUTURE
TO THE FUTURE
"whatever happened" to...
"Remember the time we...
"We used" to....
I'll never forget when we...
who was the bloke... who..
I used to have....
Lenny

THERE WAS A MAGICIAN WHOSE ACT WAS STOLEN BY HIS AUDIENCE..... WAS STOLEN BY THE WORLD AROUND HIM.

A WORLD WHICH LEARNED ALL THE SKILLS OF DECEPTION, TRICKERY, JUGGLING AND EFFECT.... A WORLD WHICH SPOKE INCREASINGLY IN BRILLIANT JOKES AND RIDDLES.

THE MAGICIAN HAD TO DEVELOP A NEW ROLE. HE DECIDED TO BECOME AN AUDIENCE. AN AUDIENCE OF ONE. AN ACT WHICH HE BUSKED ON A STREET CORNER UNANNOUNCED, UNADORNED, UNPREPARED.

THE PASSING WORLD YELLED WITTICISMS... IT PERFORMED TRICKS WITH EVERYTHING. WITH CLOTHES, HAIR, MUSIC. RELATIONSHIPS, ART, REAL-ESTATE, POLITICS, MONEY, WORDS, FOOD, HEARTS AND MINDS.

MODERN LIFE HAD BECOME AN ACT OF CUNNING EXCEPT OF COURSE THE LIFE OF THE AUDIENCE OF ONE.

THE GREATEST, TRUEST MAGICIAN OF THEM ALL

Plastic shopping bags in Autumn.

"Sorry to see you go Dad, but we wish you well in your new life."